ET TU, BRUTE?

Alan Durant

When Kris Hopkis woke up on the morning of the trial, he was annoyed that he couldn't find his copy of Shakespeare's *Julius Caesar*. He'd been reading it before he went to sleep and he was sure that he'd put the book on his bedside table before turning out the light, but it wasn't there now.

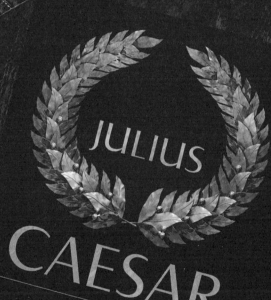

JULIUS

CAESAR

WILLIAM SHAKESPEARE

He looked on the floor next to his bed, and even underneath the bed, but there was no sign of it. He pulled back the covers, and searched beneath the clothes strewn about his room, but he still couldn't find the play. It wasn't in his school bag either.

He needed the book for English that day. He was getting more and more frustrated; the book had to be somewhere. He was reading it last night; it couldn't have just vanished into the air.

He stomped down the stairs.

'Mum, have you seen my copy of *Julius Caesar*?' he huffed.

'No, sorry', she replied, with a shake of her head.

'I can't find it anywhere. I was reading it in bed last night', Kris said, exasperated.

'We'll find it. Sit down and eat your breakfast, I'll go and have a look', soothed his mum.

Today was the start of Omar Olanbaye's trial for the fatal stabbing of fifteen-year-old Joe Tucker. *That's why he's so worked up*, she thought.

He'd been edgy ever since the murder, but more so recently with the trial looming – and with it his day in court.

Being a witness for the prosecution in a case against one of your own friends was bound to be hard.

It was no surprise that he'd got himself into a state over such a trivial thing. She searched his room thoroughly, but she couldn't find the book either. She even looked again when he'd gone to school, but it wasn't anywhere in his room.

In the end, the loss of his book wasn't too much of a problem. Kris borrowed a spare copy from his English teacher for the lesson. Anyway, there were much more important things on his mind. Well, on most people's minds.

Everyone was talking about Omar's trial.

His friends thought that he was innocent and should be acquitted. Others thought that, even if he did do it, he should be treated leniently; it was just a fight that went too far. Omar wasn't the kind of guy to stab someone deliberately.

Those who didn't know or didn't like Omar thought that he should be made an example of and given a harsh sentence – he'd taken a life and should be made to pay for it.

Joe had gone to a different school to Omar and Kris. In fact, most of the time he hadn't gone to school at all. He'd hung around the shopping centre or near the basketball court in the park, sometimes on his own, sometimes with his mates, and usually causing trouble.

Kris had had his run-ins with Joe, but who hadn't? Joe was a troublemaker.

Kris was relieved that he wasn't needed in court on the first day of the trial. He hoped that he wouldn't be needed at all – there were plenty of other witnesses. Maybe they wouldn't call him in.

He watched the news report on the trial that evening. 'The jury were told', the reporter said, 'That on April 1st in Merton Park, Omar Olanbaye got into an argument with Joe Tucker, a pupil from a rival school. This argument escalated into a physical fight between the two youths, at the end of which Omar Olanbaye was heard to threaten Joe with the words, "You're dead".

'Later that afternoon Joe Tucker was fatally stabbed on a patch of waste ground behind the block of flats where he lived. There were no witnesses, but it is alleged that Omar Olanbaye was carrying a knife that day.

'The court was told that Omar is not a violent boy and has not been in trouble with the police before. He's liked by his peers and generally thought to be considerate. The trial continues tomorrow.'

Kris wished he hadn't watched the news. He felt terrible – especially about the knife. That was his fault. The police had asked him if Omar carried a knife. He'd said 'Yes', without thinking. He wasn't lying; Omar did carry a Swiss Army knife he'd been given by his dad for his birthday.

But the only thing that Kris had ever seen him use it for was taking the top off a bottle.

He tried to explain that to the police, but they weren't interested. Omar had a knife, that's all they wanted to hear.

Omar didn't deny it, but he claimed it had gone missing a few days before the murder. The trouble was, he couldn't prove that.

The knife was being used as the key evidence against Omar and it was all Kris's fault.

Kris struggled to get to sleep that night. His copy of *Julius Caesar* hadn't turned up, so he couldn't even read that.

When he did finally drift off, he had disturbing dreams. He dreamed that someone was in his room, a dark shadowy figure whose face he couldn't see.

It was a relief to wake up. He pushed back his duvet and swung his feet on to the floor. Looking down, he froze in horror. Next to his left foot was a black footprint – just one. A perfect print, as if someone had rubbed the shoe in ink and pressed it down on the floor very carefully.

'Mum!' Kris shouted.

Kris's mum was angry at first, seeing the stain on the floor. But her anger soon turned to sympathy when she saw how hysterical Kris was. She took pity on him and tried to calm him down.

'Someone's been coming into my room while I'm asleep!' he yelled. 'It's obvious. First the book, and now this!'

His mum was sure that there had to be a rational explanation, though she couldn't think of one.

'Who would break in to take a book or leave a footprint?' she argued.

'Someone who wants to scare me', Kris replied.

'But why?'

'It must be because of the trial.'

'You think someone's trying to intimidate you to stop you testifying?'

Kris's mum shook her head in disbelief.

Kris said nothing. He just stared at the footprint with haunted eyes.

He was pretty shaken up, but Kris still went to school. He didn't want to be at home; he didn't feel safe there.

At school everyone was talking about the news report on the trial. Many of them hadn't known about Omar's knife. They were starting to change their minds about his innocence.

Kris didn't want to talk about it. He couldn't bear thinking about Omar up there in the dock, Omar alone in his prison cell, Omar, his friend ...

Kris arrived home from school to the news that he was wanted in court the next day. It was time to testify – for the prosecution. His mum had cleaned up the footprint, but Kris could still picture it as clear as day.

He couldn't eat that evening. He couldn't sit still. He wasn't just worried about testifying; he couldn't stop thinking about what might happen that night when he went to sleep. What would he find in the morning?

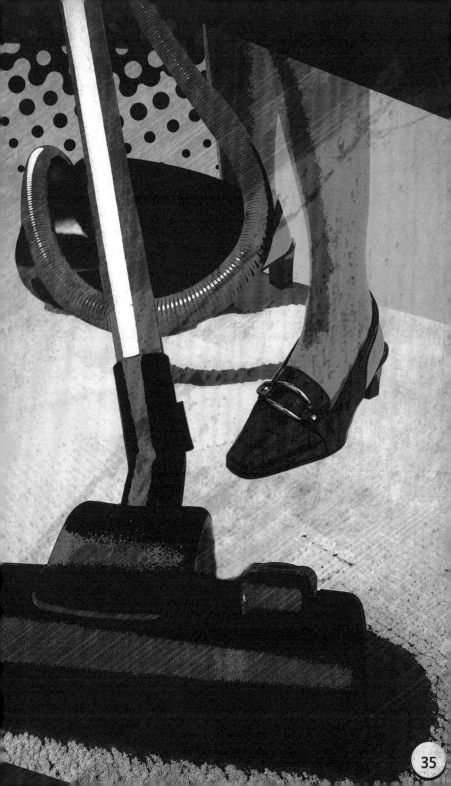

When his mum had locked up the house and gone to bed, Kris did his own security inspection. He checked all the windows, and found one in the kitchen that wasn't properly secured. That must have been how the intruder got in. He locked the window.

Now he was safe. He went to bed and fell asleep almost at once, exhausted from the intensity of the day.

When Kris opened his eyes in the morning, he thought he must still be dreaming: the *Julius Caesar* book was back. It lay open on the floor by his bed, in exactly the place where the footprint had been the previous morning.

Kris knew, without having to look, which scene in the play would be showing on the page. It was Act Three, Scene One: the murder of Julius Caesar. One line was highlighted in yellow – the most famous line in the play, Caesar's accusation of his friend Brutus: 'Et tu, Brute?' *And have you, too, betrayed me, Brutus?*

Kris stared at the open book with its three highlighted words and felt a sudden sense of calm resolution. He was going to be strong. He was going to tell the truth and nothing could stop him.

He would no longer be ruled by fear.

When he was called to the witness box a few hours later, Kris Hopkis took an oath to tell the truth. Then he looked at the judge and declared, 'It was me. I killed Joe Tucker.'

TITLES IN THE *SHOTS* SERIES

A Bird in the Hand
Anne Rooney
ISBN 9781783220205

A Man in Uniform
Alex Stewart
ISBN 9781783220236

Umbrella Fella
Lorna Read
ISBN 9781783220229

Whatever Lily Wants
Gillian Philip
ISBN 9781783220212

Et Tu, Brute?
Alan Durant
ISBN 9781783220274

No Heroics
Liz Holliday
ISBN 9781783220250

Port of Entry
Alex Stewart
ISBN 9781783220243

A Thousand Words
Gillian Philip
ISBN 9781783220267

WWW.READZONEBOOKS.COM

TITLES IN THE *ON TARGET* SERIES

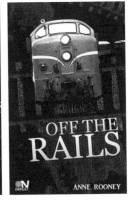
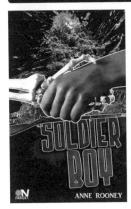